MUSIC BY
MARC BLITZSTEIN

BOOSEY & HAWKES

INTRODUCTION

This songbook is designed to bring before the public a selection of the vocal music of the seminal 20th century American composer—Marc Blitzstein. Most of the songs published here are taken from Blitzstein's stage works; some of the pieces are published for the first time and many have been long out of print. Whether composed for the lyric dramas on which much of his reputation stood or individually, Blitzstein's songs are eminently singable, as witness the recent popular recording by Dawn Upshaw of "I Wish It So" and other songs. Simplicity, clarity, humor, strong and supple melody – these salients of his music and words give Blitzstein's art its power, its compelling charm and its singular directness of purpose. We believe the reader will find a treasure trove in this book.

In *The Cradle Will Rock*, *No For An Answer*, *The Airborne*, *Regina*, *Juno*, *Reuben Reuben*, *Sacco and Vanzetti*, *Idiots First* and *The Magic Barrel*, Blitzstein (1905–1964) created a music rooted in the soil of the social revolution that marked his time. "He was the first composer to develop a convincing music-theatre idiom representative of American vernacular speech style," writes Robert J. Dietz in *The New Grove Dictionary of Music and Musicians* of Blitzstein's work: "Deeply committed to the doctrine of 'art for society's sake,' a doctrine adopted from Hanns Eisler, Bertolt Brecht and Kurt Weill, he devoted much of his talent for dramatic and musical characterization to topics of social commentary and political satire." Aaron Copland said of him that he made indigenous American opera possible.

The product of a classical musical education, first at the Curtis Institute of Music in Philadelphia, later under Nadia Boulanger in Paris and Arnold Schoenberg in Berlin, Blitzstein was also a literary writer of power and insight. It was the writer in him that led him to his topics of social commentary and political satire. This is evidenced not only in his own works, but also in his enormously popular adaptation of the Brecht-Weill *Threepenny Opera* which, in his English version, has been given an international life that promises to persist for many years to come.

The song, "Few Little English" written for Lotte Lenya, whose centenary occurred in 1998, was left in an unfinished state and has been completed by the editor of this volume. That song and many others included here have either never been performed or have been heard only infrequently since they were composed. Since Blitzstein's *Reuben Reuben* never made it to Broadway after its Boston opening, the songs from that production are largely unknown by the public.

A complete list of Blitzstein's works may be found on the Internet at <http://freespace.virgin.net/john.jansson>. Many of his original manuscripts are located at the Marc Blitzstein Archive at the State Historical Society in Madison, Wisconsin. Eric Gordon's 1989 *Mark the Music: The Life and Work of Marc Blitzstein*, St. Martin's Press, is a full, rich biography of the composer. A film concerning the by now legendary opening night of *The Cradle Will Rock* in New York City in 1937 has gone into production in 1998 under the direction of actor-writer Tim Robbins with an all star cast.

We, the nephews of Marc Blitzstein, are grateful to Leonard Lehrman, the editor, for his work on this publication.

Christopher Davis
Stephen E. Davis

CONTENTS

Cover Photo Credits

Top photograph by Carl van Vechten. Used by permission.

Middle photograph by David Diamond. Used by permission.

Bottom photograph by Ruth Orkin. Used by permission of the Ruth Orkin Photo Archive.

Illustration Credits

Reprinted by permission of the New York City Opera.

Reprinted by permission of the Vineyard Theatre.

Reprinted by permission of the New York Philharmonic.

Reprinted by permission of the American Symphony Orchestra.

Reprinted by permission of the Pacific Coast Opera.

THE NICKEL UNDER THE FOOT

from *The Cradle Will Rock*

Words & Music by
Marc Blitzstein
Editor
Leonard Lehrman

[A number of singers have performed this a minor third higher, but this is the original key.]

M-051-93344-0

Engraved & Printed in U.S.A.

* alternates from the 1950s: bandit/stinker[!]

Poco più mosso [♩ = 84]
live like hearts and flow-ers And ev-'ry day is a
won-der-land tour. O, you can dream and scheme and
cresc.
hap-pi-ly put and take, Take and put, But first be
[mf]
dim.
sure the nick-el's un-der your foot.
[that]
[mp]

Go stand on some - one's neck while you're tak - in', Cut in - to some - bod - y's
throat as you put, For ev - 'ry dream and scheme's de - pend - ing on
cresc.
3
whether all through the storm You've kept it warm
[mf]
[dim.]
[p]
The nick - el under your foot.
[that]
And if you're
[mp]
[dim.]

* Lower voice of R. H. may be played *loco* or, if necessary *8va*.

THE FREEDOM OF THE PRESS

from *The Cradle Will Rock*

Words & Music by
Marc Blitzstein
Editor
Leonard Lehrman

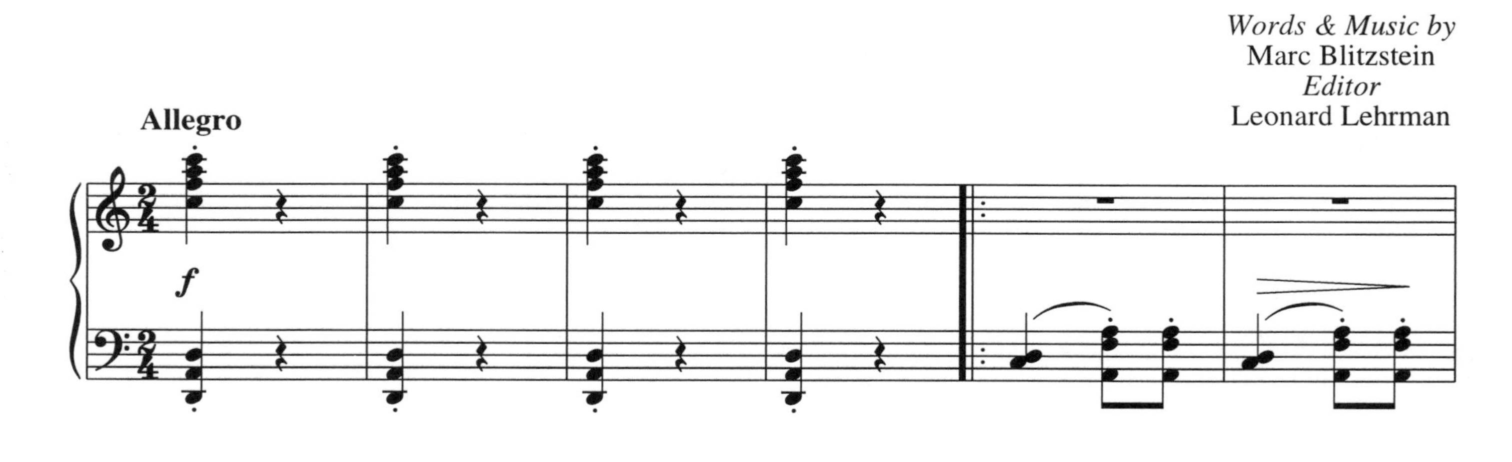

M-051-93344-0

Engraved & Printed in U.S.A.

EDITOR DAILY
All my gift at prose– 'll Be at you dis - pos - al,
Yes, we've heard of him, In fact good word of him, He
Just a min - ute, I'm not be - ing in - dis - creet! I
Mis - ter Mis - ter, you've been ver - y kind.
seems quite pop - u - lar with work - ing men.
must con - sult the own - er of my sheet.
arp. 3rd time only
MR. MISTER
I be - lieve news - pa - pers Are great men - tal shap - ers, My
Find out who he drinks with and talks with and sleeps with. And
Please don't try to cross you good hu - mored new boss. I'm the
[2. alt.: make up the rest]
steel in - dus - try is de - pen - dent on them, real - ly.
look up his past till at last you've got it on him.
own - er of your fam - ous pa - per since this morn - ing.

* alternate from 1960: labor

* 3rd time only: **EDITOR DAILY** holds note on "no." M-051-93344-0

THE CRADLE WILL ROCK

from *The Cradle Will Rock*

Words & Music by
Marc Blitzstein
Editor
Leonard Lehrman

M-051-93344-0

Engraved & Printed in U.S.A.

alt. rhythm
mark the air is chil-ly up there The sky beet-le-browed, Can
that be a cloud o-ver there? And then they put out their hands and feel
storm-y weath-er! A bird-ie ups and cries, "Boys, this looks bad.
You have-n't used your eyes. You'll wish you had. That's
[mp]
[cresc.]

Refrain
Poco più mosso
alt. rhythm
sim.
thun - der, that's light - ning and its going to sur - round you!
marcato
No won - der, those storm - birds seem to
cir - cle a - round you!
Well you can't climb down and you
Well you can't climb down and you
[1. alt.: a cer - tain]
can't sit still. That's a storm that's going to last un - til the fi - nal
can't say 'no!' You can't stop the weath - er, not with all your dough! For when the
2. alt. rhythm

1.
ff
wind blows,_ and when the wind blows ___ The cra - dle will
wind blows,_ and when the
rock!
That's
ff marcatissimo
f
2.
wind blows _ The cra - dle will rock!
ff marcatissimo
fff
The cra-dle will rock!"

CROON-SPOON

from *The Cradle Will Rock*

Words & Music by
Marc Blitzstein
Editor
Leonard Lehrman

M-051-93344-0

Engraved & Printed in U.S.A.

JUNIOR
just me and you, ba - by, I can, can-oo, ba-by, spoon? O, the
6
[mp]
croon-er's life is a bless-èd one, he makes the pop-u-la-tion hap-py. For when
alt.
SISTER
all one's cares have dis-tress-èd one O, to spoon is grand in the June-day sun, You
alt.
spoon and spoon and nev-er get tir-ed; But it's nic-er at night than in the noon-day sun, 'Cause then you're
alt.
f
alt.
8va
f

* *ad lib.:* **JUNIOR** go up to a major third above, but falsetto.

** *ad lib.:* downward gliss. to end.

JOE WORKER

from *The Cradle Will Rock*

Words & Music by
Marc Blitzstein
Editor
Leonard Lehrman

M-051-93344-0

Engraved & Printed in U.S.A.

a tempo
mf
1. Joe Work-er gets gypped. For no good rea-son, just gypped.
2. Joe Work-er just drops. Right at his work-in' he drops.
a tempo
[2nd time play R.H. an octave higher]
mf marcato
From the start, un - til the fin - ish comes, They feed him out of gar-bage cans, They
Wea - ry, wea - ry tir - ed to the core, And then if he drops out of sight, There's
breed him in the slums. Joe Work-er will go To shops where stuff is on
al - ways plen - ty more. Joe Work-er must know That some-bod-y's got him in
[1. alt.: Then he'll
show, He'll look at the meat, He'll look at the bread and too
tow. But what is the good For [just] one to be clear? O, it

look in his pock - et and just shake his head.]
[2nd time parlando]
cresc.
rit.
lit - tle to eat sort of goes to the head. One big ques-tion in -
takes a lot of Joes to make a sound you can hear! One big ques-tion in -
[loco]
a tempo
cresc. sempre
side me cries: How man-y fak - ers, peace un-der-tak - ers, paid strike-break-ers,
side me cries: How man-y frame-ups, how man-y shake-downs, lock-outs, sell-outs,
cresc. sempre
How man - y toil - ing, ail - ing, dy - ing, piled - up bod-ies, broth-er, does it take to
How man - y times ma - chine guns tell the same old stor - y, broth-er, does it take to
alt.
2nd time
1.
2.
alt.
make you wise?
make you wise?

for Lotte Lenya

FEW LITTLE ENGLISH

("Jimmy's Moll")

Words & Music by
Marc Blitzstein
edited & completed by
Leonard Lehrman

M-051-93344-0

Engraved & Printed in U.S.A.

Then they gave _ me mon - ey I got rich _ ver - y quick.
Slower
3
Then I met Jim-my and Jim-my said "gim-me!" and I gave him all I had.
That was Chi-ca-go, and you know Chi-ca-go. Well he's a Chi-ca - go lad.
Tempo I
Jim-my's not in bus' - ness, not ex-act - ly bus' - ness,

kind of mon - key bus' - ness. But he makes lots of cash
and I al - ways like that. Then he's sud - den - ly flat
rit.
and we have to eat hash. I meet the land-lord, and that's where my tricks come
3
rit.
in.
3
p
Plizz– I speak few lit - tle
p

5
Eng - lish. I'm speak-ing on - ly ver - y lit-tle few Eng - lish since I am in this
land I no un - der - stand.
rit.
rit.
Faster
mf
Well it seems my Jim - my robb'd a sec - ond stor - y
mf
in the ter - ri - to - ry of a man nam'd Ma - lone.

And it seems Ma - lone's mob they had plann'd the whole job
but Jim - my's a big snob So he went on his own.
Tempo I
He brought me two mink coats and cash en - ough to sink boats and I felt pret - ty
3
gay. But he on - ly stopp'd to kiss me and tell how he'll miss me, he's

3
rit.
Slow
sor-ry but he can't stay.
When he's gone I sit there just a lit-tle
rit.
[mp]
lone - ly.
I love Jim-my on - ly
and now Jim-my's a - way.
So what else can I say?
Suddenly! there's a ter - ri-ble din
gliss.
[mf]
and Ma-lone rush-es in,
busts in the doors and says "Where is dat punk of
3

yours!?"
p
Plizz– I speak few lit - tle
[f]
p
Eng - lish. I'm on - ly speak - ing Eng - lish a cou - ple month or
so. Hon - est– I don't know.
[mp]
[mf]
[f]
Fast mf
Ver - y soon my Jim - my sends a mes - sage to me:
mf

"Ev'-ry-thing's set, ba - by! Hop a train to you know!"
So I put my things on, all my cute paste rings on,
and my heart has wings on as I hol - ler "Hel - lo!"
Slow
mf
Two doz-en G-Men, all big heav-y he-men, sur-round me from near and far.
mf

Faster
3
3
I think, "O glo-ry, I'll tell them a stor-y, how wretch-ed and poor we are."
Tempo I
mf
"My wall-pa - per's crack - in' My bed's got no back in,
mf
pret-ty cur - tains lack - in', There's no lock on the door;
it's the ver - y top floor. I'm so ti - red at night

rit.
Slow
as I climb _ up each flight!"
They say, "Sis-ter, where you go you
won't have to climb no more."
a tempo (a little slower)
p
Please– I speak few lit - tle Eng - lish __ but now it seems my
Eng-lish is just en-ough to know,
(spoken)
O - kay, boys, let's go.
[fz]

PUREST KIND OF A GUY

("Joe's Birthday Song")
from *No For an Answer*

Words & Music by
Marc Blitzstein
Editor
Leonard Lehrman

[Original key: Paul Robeson sang this song a minor third lower and made the cut on p. 34. The original cast album made the cut on p. 36, inserting a birthday chorale on p. 38.]

M-051-93344-0

Engraved & Printed in U.S.A.

[alt. I like my win-ters warm. I like my
get it to eat and drink. I ain't the suf-fer kind, I ain't the
alt.
p
sum-mers cool. I ain't no-bo-dy's he - ro And I hear
rough-er kind, I ain't the buf-fer kind, I'm just a
tell I ain't no-bo-dy's fool.]
mf
hap-py go luck-y gink. But one thing I have got, I got a ex - tra sense. I
poco pesante
mf
alt.
[rall.]
[a tempo]
know what guys is like. I know what makes 'em click. I know what makes 'em tick, and
[tick]
[click]
[alt.]
[rall.]
[a tempo]

Slow
f
when a man's ok - ay, I know it a mile a - way.
alt.
a tempo
mf
There's the kind of
f [colla voce]
mf
sim.
man, when he pass-es by, I can tell that man's the pur-est kind of a guy.
alt. accomp. rhythm
sim.
mf
Black or white or tan ain't the rea-son why I will know that
mf
man's the pur-est kind of a guy. Go on and

alt. rhythm:
ask me how I can be cer-tain, How I can pick him out like a shot, And he will
nev-er up-set my plot By act-in' dirt-y and sly like the u-su-al guy in a
[poco rall.]
3
3
3
3
spot. Well, I don't know how I know that I know, but I know he will not! How he says hel-
[a tempo]
mf
[colla voce]
[a tempo]
mf
lo– how he says good - by– how he winks his

[alt.: Now he's
eye will show the pur-est kind of a guy. Though he's
f no push-o - ver]
[poco rall.]
ea-sy, go - in', you'll find that he knows his mind– that's the pur-est kind of a
[poco rall.]
[Allegro]
[vi - (p.38)
Allegro moderato
guy. (spoken:) Ever heard how I first met that purest kind of a guy?
I'll sing you how it was.
The rain was
rain-in' rain, the snow was snow-in' snow, it was a

stor-my night, to catch a freight on the B & O– I pulled my
alt.
alt.
cap down low, I pulled my coat up tight– I run with
alt. rhythms:
mf
all my might to hop a freight on the B & O–
alt.: a storm-y night.
I'll make it, no I can't– the
alt.: [the
[poco pesante]
mf
alt.
bulls are right be-hind the cars go rush-in' past– I run a-long the side, a
dicks are at my heels,]

ritard.
streak of light I see– a door slides o-pen wide Some-one holds out his hand to me.
[colla voce]
Can you guess?
Yes!
f [a tempo]
It's Joe. "That's the kind of man," right a-way says I to my-self, "that
Hurray for Joe!
[vi - (p. 38)
mf
[a tempo]
man's the pur-est kind of a guy!" Then I bare-ly spoke "Thank you, Joe," says
mf
mf
I and he made some lit-tle joke the pur-est kind of a guy. Now may - be

alt. rhythm:
you're just the life of the par-ty. I'll take the man I don't have to doubt, a man who
does what the oth-ers spout, I had my back to the wall, din' know what it was all a-
[poco rall.]
[a tempo]
mf
bout and when I next look a-round, I'll be bound, did-n't Joe get me out? When that kind of
[colla voce]
[a tempo]
mf
man gives the gals the eye– they kind-a trip and

run to meet that pur-est kind of a guy. O the
pur-est kind of a guy Is the dear-est kind, the sin-cer-est kind of a
[poco rall.]
[colla voce]
f
(p. 34 or 36) - de]
mf
guy. Our lit - tle pride and joy, our lit - tle
scherzando
mp
[opt. ending or insert chorale]
ba-by boy, he's kind-a look-in' up he's get-tin'

big, oh me, oh my he's got a birth - day, it is his birth - day, it is the
[that] alt.
mp
cresc.
best day for the pur-est kind of a guy. Take it from me who knows, and
Broad
f
cresc.
f
don't make no mis-take, When - ev - er there are Joes the world is on the make! And
Maestoso
ff
so, to-night, is why we give a hel - lo to the pur-est kind of a guy.
[to Joe.]
ff
ff

FRAUGHT

from *No For an Answer*

Words & Music by
Marc Blitzstein
Editor
Leonard Lehrman

M-051-93344-0

Engraved & Printed in U.S.A.

Sa-tan on-ly knows, I'm caught, tense and taut, fair-ly dis-
traught with you.
I'll be your light o-ver-head, your
mat un-der-foot,
I'm a slow creep-ing vine,
but I've
well tak-en root
for with you I am sim-ply fran-tic'-ly

fraught! you know, yes in-dee-dy boy!
Wan-ta shriek, wan-ta shout,
[arpeggiate ad lib.]
wan-ta tell the folks a-bout it! Can't keep qui-et. Though my brain's a fog,
[alt.: sil - ly]
my fool-ish tongue runs ri - ot, yes!
Hur-dy gur-dy blues I've got, o-ver-word-y blues, I've got them! Oh my dear, still and

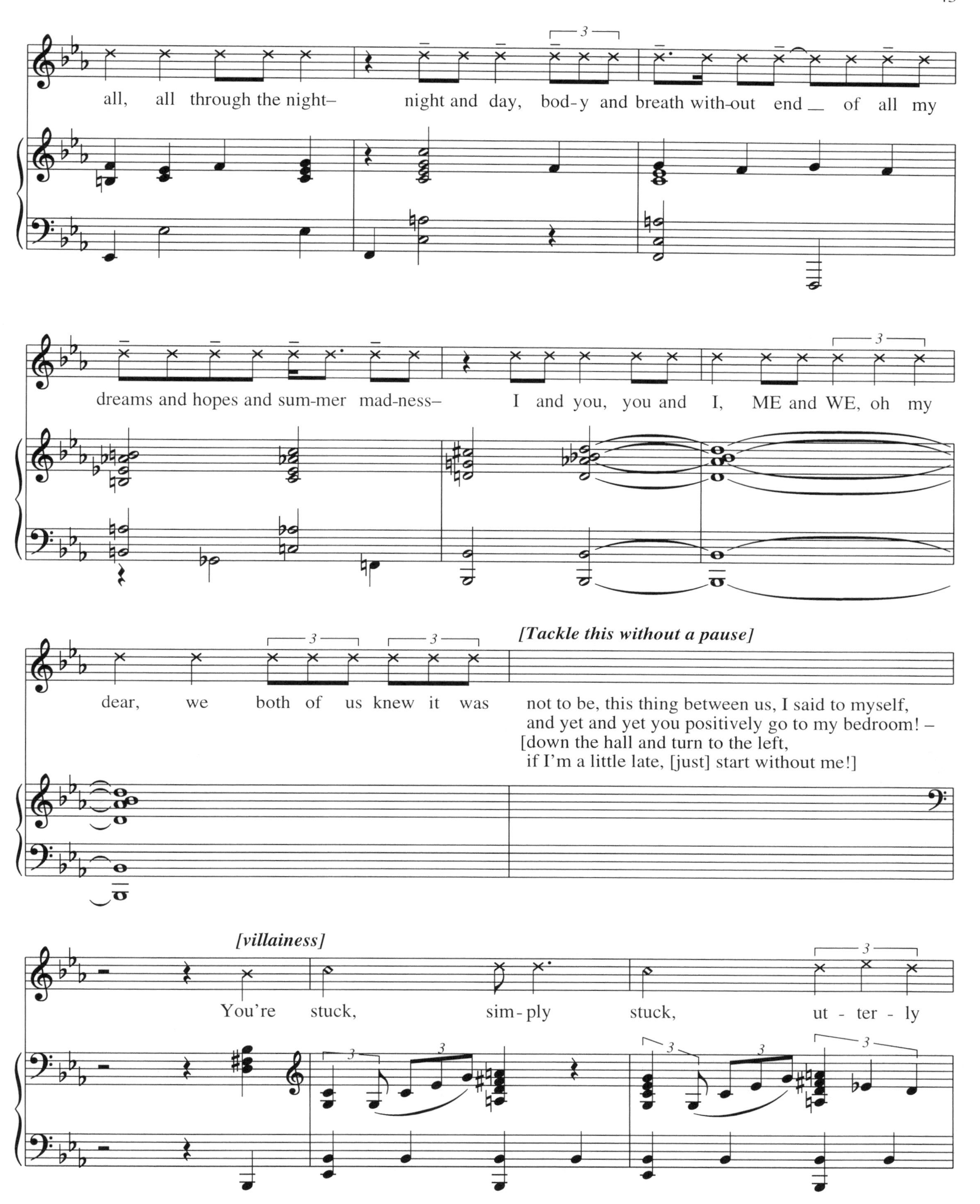
all, all through the night– night and day, bod-y and breath with-out end of all my
dreams and hopes and sum-mer mad-ness– I and you, you and I, ME and WE, oh my
dear, we both of us knew it was
[Tackle this without a pause]
not to be, this thing between us, I said to myself,
and yet and yet you positively go to my bedroom! –
[down the hall and turn to the left,
if I'm a little late, [just] start without me!]
[villainess]
You're stuck, sim-ply stuck, ut - ter - ly

stuck with me! I plan to paw you and beat you, and
taste you and eat you, I'll gorge me and glut me till no one's there but me! With
you on - ly with you just with you and I do mean you– I'm–
[it now?]
alt.: What was that word again? O yes–
[Not a fraught in my head and I frot' at the mout'-in shawt– I'm] fraught!
ff

EXPATRIATE

from *No For an Answer*

"Literary and Artistic Scene, 1928:
The place is Biarritz or the Riviera. That is, if you can afford it.
Otherwise, New Bedford or New London, Connecticut will do."

Marc Blitzstein
Music completed by
Leonard Lehrman

M-051-93344-0

Engraved & Printed in U.S.A.

It's mur - der! Life's on - ly South of France for me or
It's mur-der! O it's the South of France for me or
It - al - y– I'm home in Nice or Rome the way the Ro - mans are. I al - ways
It - a - ly– I'm home in Nice or Rome the way the Ro-mans are. I al-ways
do my roam - in' near the bar. And how! I love that
do my roam-in' near the bar. And how! I love that

cryp-tic, el-lip - tic mode of speech, Some-where's a ru-in, Some-where a beach,
Grapes and rapes with - in my reach, Oh, ain't it great, I'm an ex-pa - tri-ate!
But wait! - oh didn't they tell you, the lira's up, the dollar's down?
Poco tragico
(announcing)
Stockmarket crash blamed for failure of the
Bank of the United States, New York City.
Now we can't be an e-mi-gré the
You mean we all gotta go home?
Hem-ing - way. and walk and talk and look the way a he-ro looks
In all the

fan-cy ul-tra-mod-ern books.
My trou-bled
soul, it had a chance in South-ern France. I'm so at peace in Nice, I'm like a lit-tle child.
O you should see the lit-tle child run wild!
It's rot-ten but what can you do? For-
got-ten the way _ to tell time, ain't you?
Nev-er ear - ly, nev-er late _
3
3

What year is it, 'twen-ty - eight?
I said I nev-er, nev-er
l.h.
f
mp
want to go back home. I al-ways want to stay in Nice or Rome. But if they're gon-na make me
go back home To be re-turn'd to me home state, To go to be an
poco mosso
ex - Ex-pa - tri-ate, I'll go back– I won't ar - gue, I'll go back As for drink-in' I'll be
mf
f l.h.
mp

drink-in' I'll be stink-in', Gon-na o-pen their ho-ri-zon, With Eu - ro-pe - an civ-il - i - zin'. I'll ar-
rive with all my books and ban-ners, loud Ho-san-nahs, Drums and pia-nas, dried ba-na-nas,
p
cresc.
poco allarg.
Tempo I
my ban-dan-nas; my bad man-ners– I'll be an e - mi-gré the Hem-ing - way
f
back home!
ff

IN THE CLEAR

from *No For an Answer*

Words & Music by
Marc Blitzstein
Editor
Leonard Lehrman

N.B. On Blitzstein's own recording of this song, he has Muriel Smith sing all of verse one until the last three measures, then concludes with the last three measures of verse two.

M-051-93344-0
Engraved & Printed in U.S.A.

wild - ly hap - py first years, When you still don't know you're you. Then there
come the worst years– Those you scram-ble through– And one day you wake
alt. rhythm
up. You have lost a cer-tain joy while you've been grow - ing, You have
shed some name - less fear And you're left with know-ing That you're in the

clear. On that day you're grown up. There are no fan - fares to
alt. rhythm
non legato
hear; You're just in the clear. (Hum.)
p
pp
mp
2. You think man-y
mp
pp legatissimo
things at night And e - ven will speak them out. At night they

* Italic text appears in an earlier sketch but cut, along with the music to these five measures, in the final version.

- de
mf
cresc.
f
dim.
Pan.]
For I tell him, yes, we love your love - ly tal-ents And your
charm, it charms us too. But your charm and tal-ents sim-ply hap-pened to
you. Well, they won't see you through. You're out a - mong big - ger boys. Stop
alt. rhythm
non legato
play-ing with toys. So I'm in the clear… Hurray for me. Does it have to be so lone-ly?
p
(spoken)
(sung)
[rall.]
pp
dim.

PENNY CANDY

from *No For an Answer*

Words & Music by
Marc Blitzstein
Editor
Leonard Lehrman

"a primer in the fine art of panhandling"

I goes up to this rich woman - and right in front of her, I collapses.

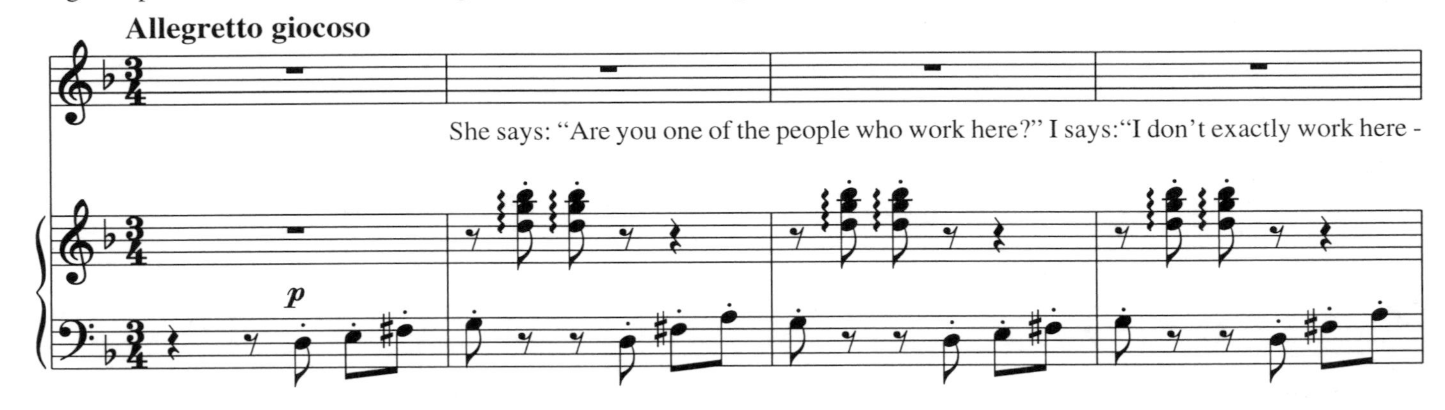

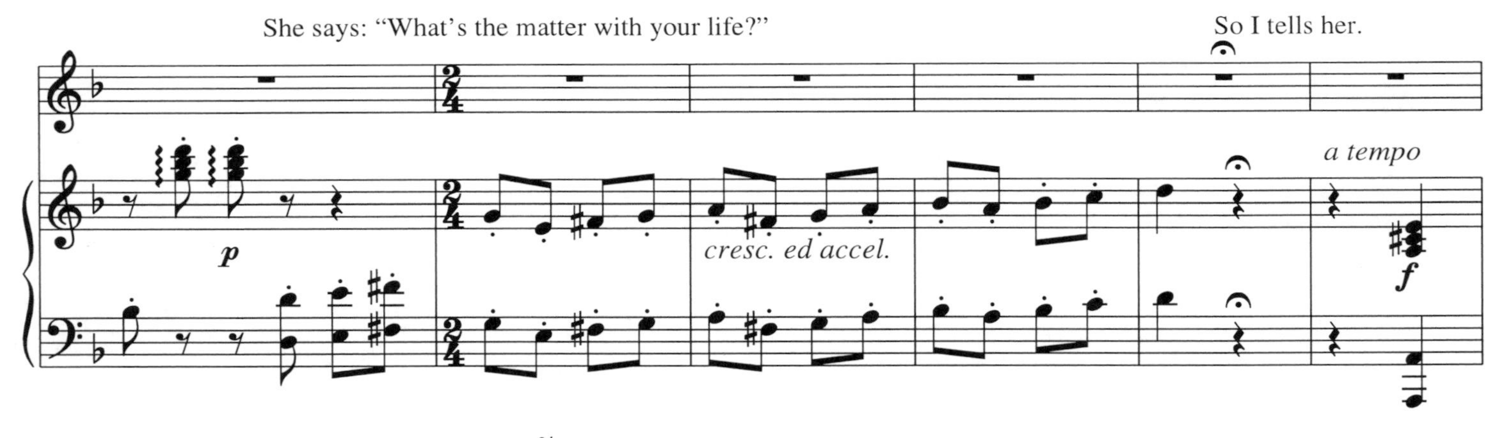

M-051-93344-0
Engraved & Printed in U.S.A.

mf parlando (ma non parlato!)
Ah, mad - am, I will spare you my tale of woe, _ You'd
p
sor - row so, _ your heart would break. There was my dar - ling moth - er, who
cursed and drank, One day she sank _ down in that lake. _ The
3
3
lake by her win - dow, and she in bed, _ by liq - uor maimed. She
[lamed]
3
3

mus - ta fell out and fell in, She's dead and still un - claimed. For
ten years we have - n't found the bo - dy...
Ah,
mad - am, I won't tell you a - bout my - self. I'm on the shelf, a
ruin - ed life. My chil - dren in the gut - ter and gar - bage grew. Their

moth-er too my wed-ded wife, and me with lum-ba-go, and
bit-ten by a spec-ial curse. All night and all day I'll be
sit-tin' by and feel-in' worse and worse– Why? I got-ta se-cret pas-sion!
(parlato)
This old wreck can still dream, mad-am. You'd nev-er guess–
She says:
f
mf
mp
pp

"Liq-uor too, I sup-pose–"
Me? Nev - er touched it!
"Rich - es?"
Naa, I don't crave rich-es.
She says:
"Wo - men?"
Real - ly, mad - am, you have mis-tak - en your
[pantomime]
man!
You'll on - ly laugh at me–
You'll think it's child - ish–

f
"What is it? Go on!" You sure?... Oh lead me
f
L'istesso tempo
to that smell of pen-ny can - dy! Al-though I ain't got an - y pen-ny
han - dy. If you will on - ly say that I may smell a spear-mint bell–
mf
p
a non-pa-reil a Scotch de-light, a taf - fy bite no, not a bite, but

just a smell. Take me a - way– I don't feel well. Oh, I go cra - zy on - ly
smell-ing when I can-not buy a thing to - day.
f
She says: "What a peculiar passion to have!"
But me, I'm an artist!
I goes right on!
I says:
mp
I guess that pen-ny can-dy has al-ways been my
f
dim.
p

set - tin' sin and se - cret vice, and though it is my shame I can
think of tons of oth - er ones not near so nice. I
once had an un - cle, was just like me– a queer ga - loot. He
fell off a der - rick and broke his knee. They had to shoot. But when they
f
f

He said: "Take it away! No chloroform!" So they said:
"Well what'll we give him?"
be-gan to chlo-ro-form him–
So he said: "Oh, lead me
mf
ad lib.
pp
to that smell of pen-ny can - dy! That's all I need to make me fine and
legatissimo
dan - dy, If you will on - ly say that I may smell them Toot-sie rolls–
p
them lic-o-rice mops– them jel-ly beans, them choc-o-late drops, For if I can-not have one
cresc.

smell, it's just as well I pass a - way to - day."
cresc.
She says: "You mean to say you really dream of penny candy? You know I think that's touching!"... Touching!...
Aha!... And now I presses to the advantage!
And
Doloroso meno mosso
Mad-am, would you guess that my eve - ry kid in - her - it - ed my love for sweets. The
mis - er-y is that I can nev-er try to sat - is - fy the lit - tle treats. For

man - y and man - y's the num - ber of pen - nies could be spent. Did you know the price of an
mp
[way]
Go on kids–
back to your gutter!
or - ange slice? It's six for a cent.
mf
mp
Tempo Iº Allegro
She says: "[Well] how many children do you have?"
[I can't talk.]
"Four." [she says.]
"Big one–
Medium
[uh - huh]
Little one
[uh!]
Babe in arms."
[no!]
"O," she says:
"The most pitiful
[p]
[pp]

story I ever heard - here, take this my poor, poor man!"
She hands me a bill. It was twenty smackers!
mf
ad lib.
poco più mosso
ff
I could - a bought out a store of pen - ny can - dy!...
[went and]
[What do you
think I did?]
ff
But me, I'm an artist!
p
[By the time I came to -
she was already
leavin'–
so]
I runs after her, and says: "Here lady, take back your money. I'll never forget ya–
for to me, madam, to me –
you're an all-day sucker."
[She says: "Go on."]
f

THE NEW SUIT

("Zipperfly")

Words & Music by
Marc Blitzstein
Editor
Leonard Lehrman

M-051-93344-0

Engraved & Printed in U.S.A.

3
etc.
goo. And the bo-dies of three dead ants, carefully laid side by side, Star-light, Star-bright, first star I see tonight,
goo. And I call up - on the seventh letter of the seventh word of the seventh paragraph of the Editorial Page of the Daily News.
A little slower
mf
I want a suit with a form-fit-tin' coat, and a six but-ton vest, and a
Grant me a suit with a form-fit-tin' coat, and a six but-ton vest, and a
mp
zip-per-fly. It will not shrink when weath-er gets storm - y. And
zip-per-fly. Oh with that fear - ful plea-sure I'll wear it. I'll
no one ev - er wore it be - fore me. No-thing could be so
be so beau-ti-ful I can't bear it. No-thing could be so

fine. A won - der - ful suit which was bought and paid for, in a
fine. And please have that suit with a pep-per and salt pat-tern And a
gen - u - ine store, with a zip-per-fly.
lit-tle place for flow-ers and a zip-per-fly.
2. alt. rhythm:
a little faster
If you had two
My dream tells me
a little faster
broth - ers, with their hand - me - downs left to you
one day, I will walk down Fifth A - ven - ue.
Then you'd know what I'm wish - ing for. You
It will be East - er Sun - day may - be.
[rall.]
3
[rall.]

a tempo
dream of your wine and your wo - men and song, and ci -
Peo - ple will pass me and nudge one - an - oth - er, and
a tempo
gars a foot - long but as for I, I dream of pants with those
say as they sly - ly give me the eye: "Who is that man in that
mod-i-fied peg cuffs and a high waist ef - fect and a zip-per-fly.
won - der-ful suit, that en - chant-ing new suit with the
1.
mp
2.
zip-per-fly?"
(Solo)
mf

[rall.]
[rall.]
mf [a tempo]
Now I lay me down to sleep, I pray the Lord my soul to keep.
[a tempo]
mp
And if be - fore I wake, I should die
Please lay me out in my
rit.
won-der-ful suit, My un - speak-a - ble suit with the zip-per-fly.
rit.

MODEST MAID

Words & Music by
Marc Blitzstein
Editor
Leonard Lehrman

M-051-93344-0
Engraved & Printed in U.S.A.

Allegro, with dash
LECH-ER - Y– Sim - ple LECH-ER - Y. If there's one thing is
LECH-ER - Y– Love - ly LECH-ER - Y. If there's one thing is
meno f
fun it is lust. Of a night in the park I am
fun it is ...you know. When the moon's at the full, I'm a
meno f
dream - ing. There am I na-ked stark, run-ning steam-ing and
mad one But don't call a con-sta - bull, for this mad one has
[a - woo!]
rit.
a tempo
scream-ing for LECH-ER - Y, love - ly LECH-ER - Y And I'll
had one. Now pru - der - y mixed with lewd - er - y Makes a
a tempo

take noth - ing else in its stead. I've tried ar-cher - y.
dish which with fla - vor is rife. You take ar-cher - y if you're
I've tried butch-er - y. I've tried witch-er - y, and nat - ur - al - ly
arch– You take butch-er - y If you're butch. Tem - per witch-er - y with wit, make with
bitch-er - y. But my mod - es - ty falls for, Pro - pri - et - y
bitch-er - y a bit. Though it may be un - sound to, I'm bound to come
cresc.
poco rit.
1.
calls for What's eas - i - er done than said. Give me
round to Just hav - ing the time of my
poco rit.
cresc.

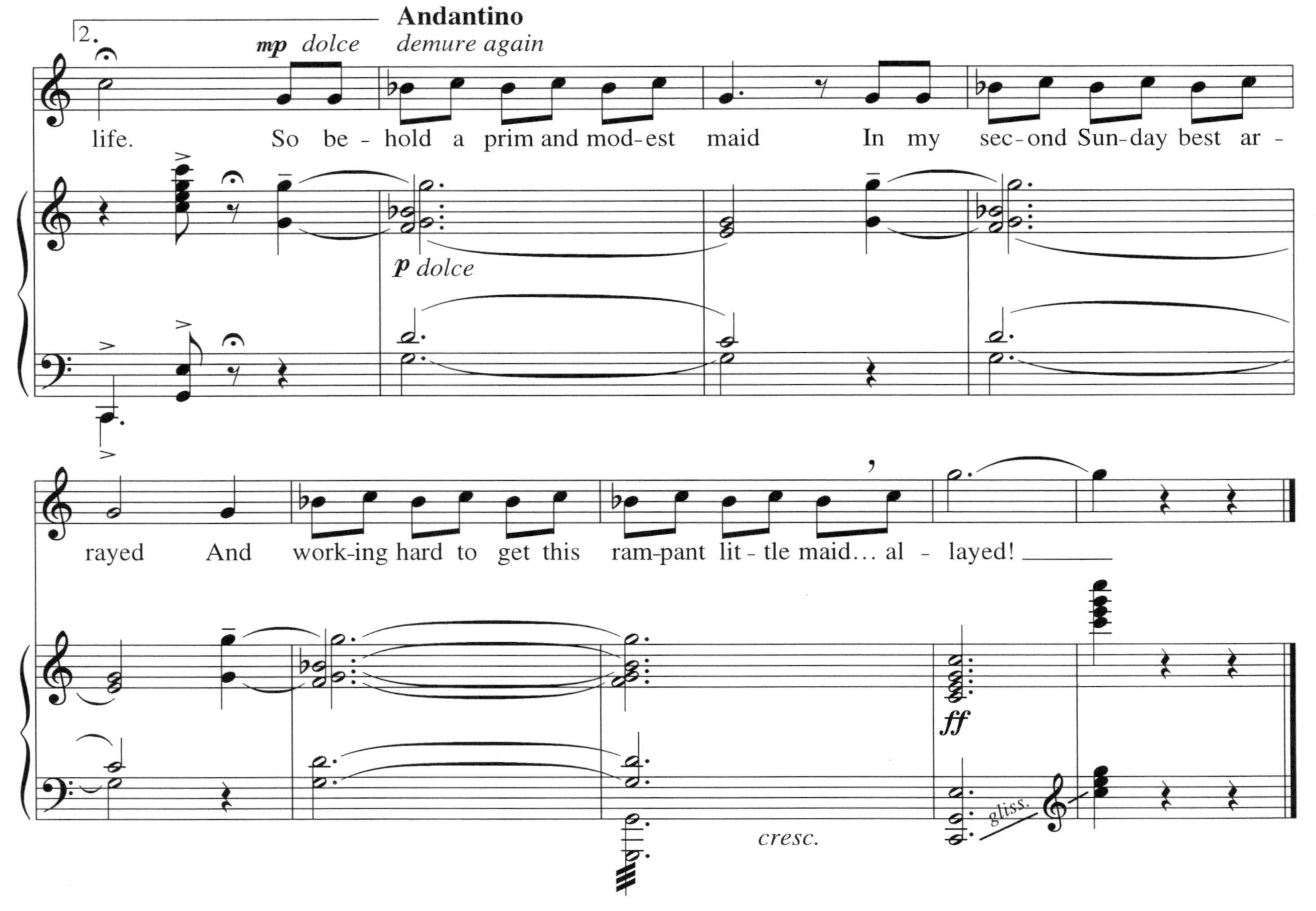

NEW YORK CITY CENTER

WINTER SEASON 1960

NEW YORK CITY OPERA

THURSDAY EVENING, FEBRUARY 11, 1960, AT 8:15 O'CLOCK

Premiere performance by the New York City Opera of
Marc Blitzstein's

THE CRADLE WILL ROCK

Cast
(In order of appearance)

Moll .... Tammy Grimes (debut)
Gent .... Seth Riggs
Dick .... Arnold Voketaitis
Cop .... Dan Merriman
Reverend Salvation .... Kenneth Smith
Editor Daily .... Jack Harrold
Yasha .... Michael Wager (debut)
Dauber .... Chandler Cowles (debut)
President Prexy .... John Macurdy
Professor Trixie .... Philip Bruns
Professor Mamie .... Maurice Stern
Professor Scoot .... Howard Fried
Dr. Specialist .... Joshua Hecht
Harry Druggist .... William Griffis (debut)
Clerk .... Lehman Engel
Mr. Mister .... Craig Timberlake
Mrs. Mister .... Ruth Kobart
Junior Mister .... Keith Kaldenberg
Sister Mister .... Nancy Dussault
Steve .... Frank Porretta
Bugs .... George Del Monte
Sadie Polock .... Sophie Ginn (debut)
Gus Polock .... Robert Kerns
Larry Foreman .... David Atkinson
Ella Hammer .... Jane A. Johnston (debut)
Reporters .... { Seth Riggs
William Saxon }

Townspeople
Conducted by Lehman Engel (debut)
Staged by Howard Da Silva (debut)
Sets by David Hays
Costumes by Ruth Morley
Dance Direction by Billy Parsons
Chorus Master: William Jonson

The action takes place in Steeltown, U.S.A., 1931, on the night of a union drive.

Scene 1: Streetcorner.
Scene 2: Nightcourt.
Scene 3: Mission.
Scene 4: Lawn of Mr. Mister's home.
Scene 5: Drugstore.
Scene 6: Hotellobby.

INTERMISSION

Scene 7: Nightcourt.
Scene 8: Facultyroom.
Scene 9: Dr. Specialist's office.
Scene 10: Nightcourt.

By arrangement with Tams-Witmark Music Library, Inc.

VINEYARD THEATRE

DOUGLAS AIBEL
Artistic Director

BARBARA ZINN KRIEGER
Executive Director

JON NAKAGAWA
Managing Director

presents

Book by
JOSEPH STEIN

Music & Lyrics by
MARC BLITZSTEIN

Based on the play *Juno and the Paycock* by
SEAN O'CASEY

with

STEPHEN LEE ANDERSON
IVAR BROGGER
JAMES CLOW
MALCOLM GETS
ANITA GILLETTE
JEANETTE LANDIS
DICK LATESSA
TANNY McDONALD
BILL NABEL
ERIN O'BRIEN
FRANK O'BRIEN
ANNE O'SULLIVAN
VERNA JEANNE PIERCE
ANDY TAYLOR

Scenic Design by
WILLIAM BARCLAY

Lighting Design by
PHIL MONAT

Costume Design by
GAIL BRASSARD

Musical Direction and Adaptation by **GRANT STURIALE**

Additional Lyrics by **ELLEN FITZHUGH**

Choreography by
JOEY McKNEELY

Sound Design by
BRUCE ELLMAN

Production Stage Manager
KENNETH J. DAVIS

Directed by
LONNY PRICE

BRUCE ELLMAN (Sound Design) has designed dozens of plays at dozens of venues including the Vineyard Theatre productions of, *Responsible Parties*, *Soulful Scream Of A Chosen Son*, *Hannah . . . 1939*, *Moving Targets*, *The Party/Lady Bracknell's Confinement*, *Nightingale* and *One Of The All-Time Greats*. Other credits include, *The Old Boy* and *Man, Woman, Dinosaur* for Playwrights Horizons; *Tea*, *Wolf-Man*, *Prin* and *Beggars In The House Of Plenty* for The Manhattan Theatre Club; *Earth And Sky* and *Jersey City* for Second Stage Theatre; *The Encanto Files And Other Short Plays*, *Niedecker*, and *Violent Peace* for The Women's Project; and dozens of plays at The Ensemble Studio Theatre of which he is a member.

DISPLACED

Words & Music by
Marc Blitzstein
Editor
Leonard Lehrman

M-051-93344-0
Engraved & Printed in U.S.A.

dim.
still, was my house!
good, my chil - dren.
What I thought,
This was work,
dim.
what I did, where I ran, where I hid,– I could not
work on work, break your back, and still work– Bit - ter work,
cresc.
tell you, not be -
nev - er meant for
cresc.
f
gin. I think I just sat down in the door-way
men. And now I am home, chil - dren, make me find the
dim.
f
dim.
where my house had been.
joy of work a - gain.
1.
2.
p
p
p

EMILY

("Ballad of the Bombardier")
from *The Airborne Symphony*

Words & Music by
Marc Blitzstein
Editor
Leonard Lehrman

M-051-93344-0

Engraved & Printed in U.S.A.

in a giv-en hour. The hand, the eye, the de-lib-er-ate brow, This
vet-er-an now sits writ-ing a let-ter home. "I take my pen in hand,
dim.
p cant.
dim.
p
Em-i-ly, To make you un-der-stand What you are to me.
p
p
I write as far as 'Dear Em-i-ly,' And can-not make it clear What you
p
p

cresc.
are to me. You are my heart's one cry. Fool-ish words that I
cresc.
wish to say and try so ter-ri-bly.
dim.
The words are like a
dim.
wall, Em-i-ly, I can-not write at all What you are to me.
p
p
cresc.
You are my heart's one cry, If you were near - by you could tell me
cresc.

why, so eas - i - ly.
Write me you will be true, Em - i - ly.
p
Write me I am to you What you are to me." At
p
dolce
night a white-faced nine - teen - year - old bom - bar - dier sits writ - ing. The
p dolce
dim.
won - der of his crew to - night, Be - fore the flight, sits writ - ting.
dim.

BLUES

from *Regina*

Words & Music by
Marc Blitzstein
Editor
Leonard Lehrman

M-051-93344-0

Engraved & Printed in U.S.A.

Rub - bing out mem - o - ries. Sleep, my ba - by. Till what the day may be
Night brush - es by on wings. Sleep, my ba - by. Why is the gown al - ways
bring - ing, here's sing - ing. If you was
dark blue? I'll tell you. May - be you
mf
Refrain (Slow Blues)
espress.
like the night, and you could see the things there
knows the woes that mak - ing folks so blue to -
are, If you was like the night, and
night. May - be you knows the woes that
8va
p
cresc.

you could see the things there are
mak - ing folks so blue to - night.
8va
dim.
p
Then you'd be blue, like you ain't nev - er been be -
Then let your own a - lone, and they'll go out, just
(2nd time)
8va
(2nd time)
fore so far.
like the night.
Tempo Iº
Night could be time to sleep.
p
Night could be time to weep.
Sleep, my ba - by.
p

WHAT WILL IT BE?

from *Regina*

Words & Music by
Marc Blitzstein
Editor
Leonard Lehrman

M-051-93344-0

Engraved & Printed in U.S.A.

feel to real - ly love a per - fect stran - ger? Look in his
eyes, and look, and kiss that per - fect stran - ger? I can - not i -
mag - ine it quite.
mp
It's like noth - ing else be - fore, The
p
3
cresc.
allarg.
a tempo
op - en - ing of a door to the light.
I stand at the
cresc.
allarg.
a tempo

door, and wait, And won-der who'll come knock-ing. Who'll stand out-
side, and wait, And won-der– will I o-pen? O-pen to what
cresc. e rit.
dazz-ling light? a tempo My life is wait-ing for me.
f
dim. rit. mp a tempo rit.
I won-der what will it be?
8va
dim. rit. p a tempo rit. pp

THE BEST THING OF ALL

from *Regina*

Words & Music by
Marc Blitzstein
Editor
Leonard Lehrman

M-051-93344-0

Engraved & Printed in U.S.A.

want and to take is the best thing of all!
Now some in the crowd hol-ler loud how they
want some-thing, and want it a lot. They *don't* know what they want– and they
hunt– and for what? Then there are a few– just a few– Oh, they
mf
f
mp

knew pret-ty well what to pur-sue; But mum - bled and fum - bled, and
lost it all.
And how a -
bout those so - lemn
he - roes in the sto - ry
Who fought the fight, and died in glo - ry?
They nev - er
mf
mp

lived to tell their ve - ry heart's de - si - re.
They mere - ly fell in - to the fi - re.
rit.
a tempo
f
We for - get them,
and we let them fall.
ff Poco maestoso
The best thing of all, is to
want–
Is to want some-thing with all of your heart, To

mf
aim, with no shame, With a true aim at the start, And if you are
mf
mp
rit.
good, ve - ry good, When the mo - ment's near - ly up - on you—
rit.
ff a tempo
riten.
Take that mo - ment, and you've got the best thing of
ff a tempo
mf riten.
a tempo
all!
8va
8va
ff a tempo
l.h.

PHILHARMONIC HALL | LINCOLN CENTER

New York Philharmonic

LEONARD BERNSTEIN, *Music Director*

ONE HUNDRED TWENTY-FIFTH SEASON 1966-1967

Thursday Evening, October 13, 1966, at 8:30
Friday Afternoon, October 14, 1966, at 2:15
Saturday Evening, October 15, 1966, at 8:30
Monday Evening, October 17, 1966, at 7:30

7168th, 7169th, 7170th and 7171st Concerts

Leonard Bernstein, *Conductor*

VERA ZORINA, *Narrator*
ROBERT HOOKS, *Narrator*
ANDREA VELIS, *Tenor*
DAVID WATSON, *Baritone*
CHORAL ART SOCIETY,
William Jonson, *Director*

SYMPHONIC FORMS IN THE TWENTIETH CENTURY—XV

SCHOENBERG Chamber Symphony No. 2, Opus 38

I Adagio
II Con fuoco

SCHOENBERG "A Survivor from Warsaw"

VERA ZORINA
CHORAL ART SOCIETY

INTERMISSION

BLITZSTEIN "The Airborne" Symphony

I
1. Theory of Flight
2. Ballad of History and Mythology
3. Kittyhawk
4. The Airborne

II
5. The Enemy
6. Threat and Approach
7. Ballad of the Cities
8. Morning Poem

III
9. Ballad of Hurryup
10. Night Music, Ballad of the Bombardier
11. Chorus of the Rendezvous
12. The Open Sky

ROBERT HOOKS
ANDREA VELIS
DAVID WATSON
CHORAL ART SOCIETY

Steinway Piano Columbia Records

The taking of photographs and the use of recording equipment in this auditorium is not allowed.

BE WITH ME

from *Reuben Reuben*

Words & Music by
Marc Blitzstein
Editor
Leonard Lehrman

M-051-93344-0

Engraved & Printed in U.S.A.

dim.
mp
You'll put them to - geth- er,
May-be there's a
man. But
make
it
soon.
dim.
p
cresc.
mp
Make
it
soon.
Now that I have found you,
you'd bet - ter make it
soon.
cresc.
p
cresc.
mf
mp
On-ly you can teach me
all I have to
be
If
you will
be with
me– If
mp
p
you will be
with
me.
p
dim.
pp
[opt.: Segue]

SUCH A LITTLE WHILE

from *Reuben Reuben*

Words & Music by
Marc Blitzstein
Editor
Leonard Lehrman

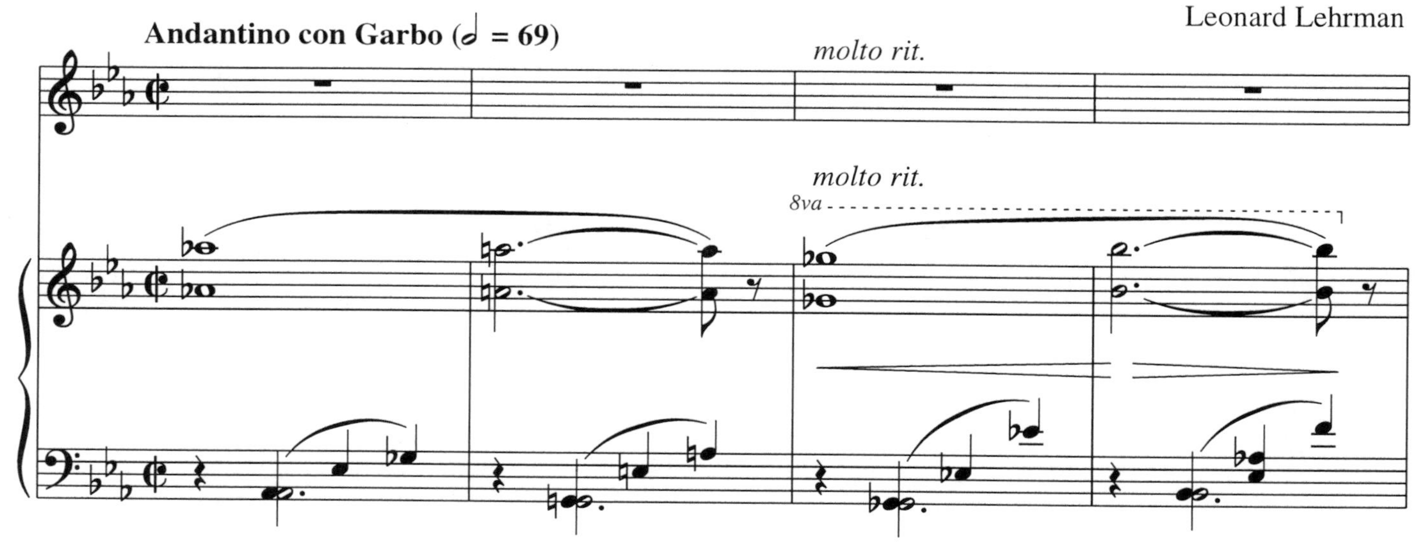

M-051-93344-0

Engraved & Printed in U.S.A.

way for two peo-ple to meet, No in-tro-duc-tion at all.
I picked you up or may-be it was you picked me. I was
rit.
there-a-lone, now You're here. And it's sud-den-ly "We."
rit.
a tempo
It just goes to show, you know, what's com-ing you don't
a tempo

know. I'm sure I will look back on this and smile.
cresc.
dim.
You will too, I guess, But I guess I should-n't
cresc.
dim.
rit.
guess. Be-cause I've know you on-ly such a lit-tle
rit.
a tempo
p
while.
a tempo
pp

THE ROSE SONG

from *Reuben Reuben*

Words & Music by
Marc Blitzstein
Editor
Leonard Lehrman

M-051-93344-0

Engraved & Printed in U.S.A.

mp
hand. Is there a song To dare the sun - light and bid re -
joice? Is there a song? It needs your voice. Your
mf
mp
dim.
hand and the sound of your voice. Is there a gown To ri - val
dim.
p
moon - light With mis - ty lace? Is there a gown? It needs your

mf
dim.
face. Your face, your voice, your hand. And
mf
dim.
[𝄾]
3
p
you, will you un - der - stand That, like the rose, and like the
pp
song too, I wait for you. And like the gown I seek your
mf
3
face. Oh, you who were fash - ioned to crown A
mf

dim.
3
rose and a song and a gown. A
dim.
rose and a song and a gown.
p
mf
f

ff
ff
rit.
rit.
mf
mp
p
pp
A rose and a song and a
gown. Here is the rose and here are you.
mp
p
pp
pp

CARNEGIE HALL
1988-89 SEASON

CARNEGIE HALL presents

American Composers Orchestra

DENNIS RUSSELL DAVIES, *Principal Conductor and Music Advisor*
Paul Lustig Dunkel, *Resident Conductor*
Robert Beaser, *Composer-in-Residence*

Sunday Afternoon, October 9, 1988, at 3:00

Dennis Russell Davies, *Conductor*

PETER WEXLER, *Director*
MILAGRO VARGAS, *Mezzo-Soprano*
DAMON EVANS, *Tenor*
GREGG SMITH SINGERS
MORGAN STATE UNIVERSITY SINGERS

STEPHEN SONDHEIM — Stavisky Suite
(Jonathan Tunick, Orchestration, World Premiere)

MARC BLITZSTEIN — Orchestra Variations
(World Premiere)

Intermission

KURT WEILL/ MAXWELL ANDERSON — "Lost In the Stars" A Concert Sequence devised by David Drew (World Premiere)

I The Hills of Ixopo
II Train to Johannesburg
III Who'll Buy
IV Murder in Parkwold/Fear
V Trouble Man
VI Cry the Beloved Country
VII Gold
VIII Big Mole
IX The Wild Justice
X Vigil and Hymn—A Bird of Passage
XI Four O'Clock
XII Reprise

PETER WEXLER, *Director*
MILAGRO VARGAS, *Mezzo-Soprano*
DAMON EVANS, *Tenor*
GREGG SMITH SINGERS
MORGAN STATE UNIVERSITY SINGERS

I WISH IT SO

from *Juno*

Words & Music by
Marc Blitzstein
Editor
Leonard Lehrman

M-051-93344-0

Engraved & Printed in U.S.A.

sleep - in' at night, And my heart beats so loud that I wake. All
a tempo
cresc.
diz - zy and light With the dream - in' and feel - in' this ache. Such a
a tempo
rit.
a tempo
dim.
thump - in' in - side me, That I think I'll go mad.
cresc.
rit.
dim.
a tempo
Andante sonore
riten.
mf
a tempo
For I wish it so! What I wish I still don't
mp
riten.
a tempo

know. But it's bound to come Though so long to wait.
I keep say - ing "To - night!" or "To - day," through the end - less
8va
days And my heart clam-ors and prays it will not come too late!
8va
(♭)
[cresc.
But when come it does, In the shape of love or

dim.]
life, I will give my life, And my love, I know. I've such
grand aims, with so ma - ny names, that I grow numb, But sure, one is
cresc.
bound to come! Be - cause I wish, I wish
f
dim.
it so. so.
alt. for cut
vi -

p
p
p
I wish it so.
(♪ = ♩ prec.)
It's the un-rest in-side me, And I think I'll go mad.
pp
- de

ONE KIND WORD

from *Juno*

Words & Music by
Marc Blitzstein
Editor
Leonard Lehrman

M-051-93344-0

Engraved & Printed in U.S.A.

found you? It was a hap-py time, I say. And at the time you did a-
gree. You did per-mit my arms a-round you. They are the same good arms to-
day. But on-ly bit-ter-ness have you for me now. Ah Ma-ry, will you give us
mf
mp
one kind word? By what en-trea-ty can you be stirred? How shall I try to pierce the

heart in you? Who is this oth - er? Tell me what the man can do. I can do it
too. Ay, more, by a third, just give us one kind word. Now you're a -
rit.
Poco meno
bout to speak: Don't do it. The bit- ter word a- gain, I'm sure. And do you
want my heart to break? You turn a - way your cheek: I knew it! You're deaf to
p
f

rit.
ev - 'ry o - ver - ture, Well, let it be a wed-ding, or a wake, then!
Tempo Iº
Ah Ma-ry, will you give us one kind word? Look, I was daft then, and naught's oc - curred!
Please have some pi-ty, I have lost my wit. Say that you'll have me. Take my love that's in-fin-ite;
Wipe the floor with it! One word, ah Ma-ry, give us one kind word.
a tempo

MARY: There's no someone else, Jerry — at least I haven't met up with him yet.

MARY: You won't be long findin' a girl far better than I am for your sweetheart, an' someone willin' to take you

as you are. I'm just not as fond of you as you'd like me to be.
I'd be deceivin' you, Jerry, if I told you diff'rent. An' that's the whole of it.

MARY: Ah Jerry, it's not just a drop of kindness you're after. I don't think you need me or anyone

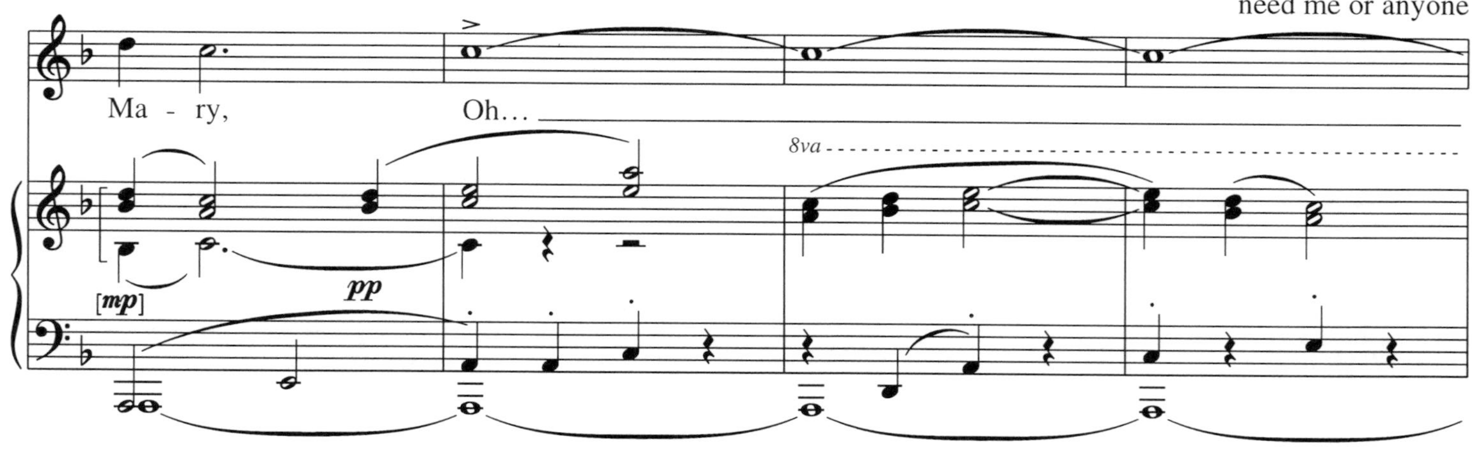

that much. You're always been glib an' light o' speech, an' sometimes I think you're fooled by your own
8va
smoothness. I'm not that deep in your heart, Jerry — an' if you don't know it, I do.
8va
mf **MARY:** I *can't* give you what you want, an' you won't be happy with just –
Give us one
mp
kind word.
pp

BIRD UPON THE TREE

from *Juno*

Words & Music by
Marc Blitzstein
Editor
Leonard Lehrman

M-051-93344-0

Engraved & Printed in U.S.A.

wind and rush-ing rain, That swayed the nest a-gain and a-
wind and rush-ing rain, That swayed the nest a-gain and a-
poco cresc.
gain. All beat-en back, its feath-ers wet, The bird was tru-ly sore be-
dim.
gain. All beat-en back, its feath-ers wet, The bird was tru-ly sore be-
dim.
dim.
rit.
mp a tempo
set. The rain was still, the wind died down. The nest re-
rit.
mp a tempo
set. The rain was still, the wind died down. The nest re-
rit.
a tempo
p

cresc.
f
mained up-on the tree. And then a strange mir - a - cle did hap - pen: The bird looked
cresc.
f
mained up-on the tree. And then a strange mir - a - cle did hap - pen: The bird looked
mf
mp
down, and was free. Ah yes, 'twas the storm it - self that did
mp
down, and was free. Ah yes, 'twas the storm it - self that did
p
p
free The bird up - on the tree.
p
free The bird up - on the tree.
p
pp

SEGERSTROM HALL

March 16, 23, 27 and 29 at 8:00pm and March 31, 1996 at 2:00pm
Preview Lecture One Hour Before Each Performance

ORANGE COUNTY PERFORMING ARTS CENTER

Dr. David DiChiera, General Director
presents
AMERICAN PREMIERE OF THE ORIGINAL STAGE VERSION

Opera in three acts
Music and text by Marc Blitzstein
After the play *The Little Foxes* by Lillian Hellman
Version for Scottish Opera
Original version restored by Tommy Krasker & John Mauceri
Broadway version premiere on October 31, 1949
Premiere in operatic scoring at New York City Center, 1953

Conductor	JOHN MAUCERI
Director	ARTHUR MASELLA
Chorusmaster	HENRI VENANZI
Choreographer	PEGGY HICKEY
Set Designer	JAMES L. JOY
Costume Designer	JOSEPH A. CITARELLA
Lighting Designer	STEPHEN ROSS
Wig and Makeup Design	ELSEN ASSOCIATES

CAST

Regina Giddens	CAROL NEBLETT
Alexandra Giddens (Zan)	RENEE SOUSA*
Birdie Bagtry Hubbard	SHERI GREENAWALD
Addie	KARLA BURNS
Horace Giddens	JOHN STEPHENS
Ben Hubbard	BRIAN STEELE
Oscar Hubbard	JAMES MADDALENA
Leo Hubbard	SCOTT PIPER GÓMEZ*
Cal	KIRK WALKER
William Marshall	CHRISTOPHER CAMPBELL
Jazz	DAMON EVANS

Party guests and servants

* Member of Opera Pacific Apprentice Artists Program

Performed in English with supertitles.
The opera will be performed with two 20-minute intermissions. Total running time is approximately 3 hours and 15 minutes.

Opera Pacific wishes to acknowledge the generosity of the following underwriters:
DONNA and JOHN CREAN
who have underwritten this production of *Regina.*

THE HONORABLE BETTY LOU LAMOREAUX and ELIZABETH SAMSON
for underwriting the supertitles.

WITH A WOMAN TO BE

from *Sacco and Vanzetti*

Words & Music by
Marc Blitzstein
Editor
Leonard Lehrman

[original key a whole tone higher]

M-051-93344-0

Engraved & Printed in U.S.A.

ring her bell, And she put on her hat, We take a walk, Go by
Mil - ford Park, Feed the pi - geons– nice.
With a
wo-man to be, With a wo-man to be, With a wo-man to be.
We
come back home, Ver-y tired we sit on the steps her a - part - ment.
She
mp
p
r. h.
poco

cresc.
ask me in, I open the door and she go in before me. She
poco cresc.
go in the kitchen. I stand and wait in the vestibule Till she
poco rit.
a tempo ♩ = ♩. prec.
mf
a piacere
say come in. She is wearing blue-suit, She
mf
dim.
don't take off her hat. The shoes, brown shoes, They make her looking
dim.

cresc.
nice. I see how she look, And how she is pret - ty.
cresc.
deciso
cresc.
f
rit.
Heart, you close my mouth I can-not to speak. O-pen up my mouth. Now I have to speak:
deciso
cresc.
f
rit.
a tempo
più f appassionato, con moto
poco a
Ro - sa, I ask her, Tell me yes. Tell me
[O Ro - sa,]
f
poco a
poco dim.
f
yes, I want to hear yes. She say she don't know, She
poco dim.
mf

riten.
a tempo
dim.
cresc.
meno f
need time, She must think. Ro - sa, when I think
dim.
wo - man, When I think wo - man, I on - ly think
mp
rit.
mp dolciss.
Andante cantando
mp
mp
you. My com - pan-ion-ship, My com-rade-ship, I put my
dolciss.
p
heart here un - der you. Look down and take it

mf
to
you.
If you need
all the time to
mp
think
Spend your time
when you think our
ba - bies
That
we make:
Dan - te
and
I - nes.
poco a poco cresc.
Think
Dan - te,
poco a poco cresc.
riten.
ff
I - nes,
And
that's all–
No-thing else. A - mo
- re,
f

No - thing else.
I tell you all you
need to see:
poco cresc.
dim.
How it is good for
me
mp
With a wo-man to be, With a
♩. = ♩ prec.
Tempo primo ♩. = 72
p
wo-man to be, With a wo-man to be.
rit.
pp
pp

HOW I MET MY NEW GRANDFATHER

from *Idiots First*

Marc Blitzstein
edited & completed by
Leonard Lehrman

* Begin here for solo version, playing Itzak's part in the accompaniment.

M-051-93344-0

Engraved & Printed in U.S.A.

* Changed in accordance Bernard Malamud's wishes, Jan 6, 1974.

[orig.: don't move]
[Big and fierce, a
Not a move, the face is still, It sits there. Fierce the nose, and
fierce mus-tache, The]
poco cresc.
fierce the mus-tache, fierce eye-brows too. This ban-dit my gra-mom-ma wed.
poco cresc.
f
Then she pushed me on him, that she said: Here he is, Your grand-son
mp
p
mf
mf (Suspense)
Ooh, ya ya ya Ah ya ya yaï!
dim.
p
Men-de-le. Such a fear,
p
mp
pp

* Change from original recommended by Leonard Bernstein, Jan. 17, 1974.

Tempo di allegro moderato (♩ = 104)
[And he reached with a]
cresc.
A - yóh, I nod the head;
And he held out a big hair-y hand.
Then he said: give me a ci-gar - ret- til.
sub. p
poco stringendo
Such a
a tempo
rit.
fear, Kin - der, what a thing is such a fear.
[chil - dren]
Lo stesso
(Holds out his hand)
Ooh! Ci-ga - ret-til?
It-zak, you know you don't smoke.
vi - (cut for solo version.)
- de

THEN

from *The Magic Barrel*

Words & Music by
Marc Blitzstein
Editor
Leonard Lehrman

M-051-93344-0

Engraved & Printed in U.S.A.

cresc.
wait-ing for an - y ex - plo-sion, and I don't care when. I'll bet they're
tell-ing the same ex-act sto - ry a - gain and a - gain. They're ei - ther
cresc.
mf
wrong. It's not meant for me. How long,
wrong, or they don't mean me. How long,
cresc.
f dim.
how old must I get to be, till for me
how old must I get to be, till for me
cresc.
dim.
mp
[rit.]
it's then?
it's then?
[rit.]
p

NOTES BY THE EDITOR

I was not lucky enough to have known Marc Blitzstein personally. But through the friendship and encouragement of four wonderful individuals now deceased, who knew him and his work intimately (Elie Siegmeister, Leonard Bernstein, Bernard Malamud, and especially Blitzstein's sister Josephine Davis), I came to know and to prize his achievements, and am proud to have been invited to edit this first publication of his collected songs, as well as the forthcoming Greenwood Press bio-bibliography of this still underappreciated composer.

Every song in this book has been reviewed with reference to available variants, and some possible alternatives are indicated by the use of brackets in the editing. Editorial choices have been based on performance practices, as reflected in recordings Blitzstein made himself (which often differed from the printed scores), sketches, and choices made by his collaborators.

All the songs in this volume were written to the composer's own texts, for Blitzstein rarely collaborated with another lyricist after his first two operas, *Triple Sec* (1928, with Ronald Jeans) and *Parabola and Circula* (1929, with George Whitsett—still unproduced). Aside from a contest piece with a text by Alfred Hayes, and a poem by Blitzstein's wife Eva Goldbeck—along with a few Elizabethan verses for use in Shakespeare plays—poems by Walt Whitman, e. e. cummings, and Dorothy Parker appear to have been the only texts (besides his own) to have inspired him as a composer. In his own compositions, the music often came much more quickly than the texts—in his quasi-autobiographical song-play *I've Got the Tune,* his alter ego Mr. Musiker admits, "...the words fail me..."—and he agonized over changes in lyrics.

To others' music, though, he often found words that were better than those with which the notes had originally been conceived: he rewrote the libretto to Ned Rorem's opera *The Robbers* and the lyrics to Leonard Bernstein's "Dream With Me" (from *Peter Pan*). He also wrote translation/adaptations of Offenbach operetta arias and duets, the Brecht-Weill *Threepenny Opera*, the Brecht-Eisler song "On Killing," and the Brecht-Dessau *Mother Courage,* the latter still unproduced. His voluminous sketches for a *Mahagonny* translation, never completed, would make a worthy subject for a dissertation.

"Bert Brecht" was the inspiration for and dedicatee of Blitzstein's first great success, *The Cradle Will Rock.* In 1937 both the federal government and Actors Equity would try to close it, but the show opened anyway, in a "concert" that spawned John Houseman's and Orson Welles' Mercury Theatre. The first orchestral performance had to wait ten years for Leonard Bernstein and the New York City Symphony. The New York City Opera staged it with full orchestra in 1960. Most productions (and all commercial recordings to date) have been with piano, the only exceptions being those with small orchestras conducted by this writer at Harvard in 1969 and by Gershon Kingsley in Gelsenkirchen, Germany in 1984.

Hearing the song of the prostitute, "The Nickel Under the Foot," at a party in New York in January 1936, Brecht suggested that Blitzstein take the image of literal prostitution and broaden it as a metaphor to express "the sell-out of one's talents, one's dignity and integrity" under capitalism. This would become a theme in much of Blitzstein's work for the rest of his life. It is best seen in "The Freedom of the Press" and other portraits in *Cradle* of middle-class types like Rev. Salvation, Yasha the violinist, Dauber the artist, President Prexy of College University, and Dr. Specialist. Only the union leader Larry Foreman, who sings the title song (printed here with the ending from its triumphant reprise version as the finale of the show), proves incorruptible. Originally he was called Larry Sickle: the song "Joe Worker" (originally titled "Poor People"—the earliest of Blitzstein's songs that he would incorporate into *Cradle*) is sung by—the logical counterpart—Ella Hammer. "Croon Spoon," sung by Sister Mister and Junior Mister, the indolent children of the tycoon Mister Mister, is a takeoff on escapist "June Moon" songs of an earlier era.

The *Cradle* songs have been grouped together, though they were written over a two-year period (most of them in six weeks in 1936, but two of them the previous year). In between Blitzstein developed an appreciation of Kurt Weill and his wife Lotte Lenya (who were at that point divorced, though they latter remarried each other), and composed the most Weillian song he ever wrote, for her: "Jimmy's Moll" or "Few Little English." Recently discovered among Lenya's papers at Yale, it appears to have been performed by her in 1938 at Le Ruban Bleu in New York, and then forgotten, left in various conflicting versions. (For details, see *Kurt Weill Newsletter* 15:2 (Fall 1997) pp. 8-12.)

No For an Answer, an anti-fascist, anti-war labor opera, was presented with piano accompaniment at the Mecca Temple (later City Center) in New York on three Monday evenings in January 1941. It has never been staged since in its entirety, though four of the five songs included here have been performed and recorded by such artists as Carol Channing, Curt Conway, Sherrill Milnes, Charlotte Rae, Paul Robeson, William Sharp, Joshua Shelley, Muriel Smith, Dawn Upshaw, and Helene Williams. The fifth one, "Expatriate," which is included in the libretto distributed by Tams-Witmark, was sketched musically several times, but apparently never written out before it was cut. (Other cut numbers were later restored in subsequent concert versions.) It has been completed and performed by the editor, to date, in Madison, Fontainebleau, and New York.

"The New Suit" (aka "Zipperfly") appears to be a remnant from the otherwise lost *New York Opera.* The monolog of a 14-year-old shoeshine boy originally written for but never performed by Jimmy Savo, it became a specialty number at parties, often sung at the piano by Leonard Bernstein (who premiered it in public in 1985), Jack Gottlieb, Michael Barrett, and Michael Tilson Thomas (Blitzstein's second cousin). Its first recording was by this writer, on Premier's 1990 CD *A Blitzstein Cabaret.*

"Modest Maid," originally written for but never performed by Beatrice Lillie, has become a widely-performed specialty number for Charlotte Rae (in *The Littlest Revue* and the LP *Songs I Taught My Mother*), Ellen Geer, and Helene Williams.

"Displaced" (aka "Song of the D.P.") is probably from *Goloopchik*, a collaboration with Jerome Robbins on American-Soviet friendship, which died at the advent of the Cold War. Recorded by Muriel Smith and the composer for Concert Hall and later by William Sharp and Steven Blier for Koch, it tells the story of a woman returning from a concentration camp by way of a displaced persons (D.P.) camp after World War II. In its reference to work, it recalls the perverse Nazi slogan: "Arbeit macht frei." Its Russian, Jewish character inspired Blitzstein to reuse the music in the Fishbein Scene (Scene 3) of *Idiots First.*

"Emily," a romantic ballad, is from *The Airborne Symphony*, a work composed during World War II and commissioned by the Eighth Army Air Force while Blitzstein was serving as a non-commissioned officer in England.

Three selections are included from *Regina*, based on Lillian Hellman's play *The Little Foxes*. "Blues," in its first version, which appears here, and was recorded by William Sharp, was originally to be sung by Cal, a role first performed by William Warfield; a later version, which appears in the full score, was given to the character of Addie to sing. Regina's daughter Zan's "What Will It Be" was called the best tune of the year by the *New York Daily News*. "The Best Thing of All" is the title character's great chance to shine—"my 'Toreador Song,'" it was called by Brenda Lewis, who took over the role from Jane Pickens when the work moved from Broadway to the opera house.

Reuben Reuben, an urban folk opera study of a young man (created by Eddie Albert) with aphonia (loss of voice due to psychological causes such as hysteria) and the young woman (Evelyn Lear, in her professional singing debut) whose love rescues him from himself, died of book problems in Boston. But much of its music is worth savoring, or reusing, as Blitzstein had planned and begun to do in *Sacco and Vanzetti*. "The Rose Song," as recorded by William Sharp or Ronald Edwards, is a worthy successor to Weill's "September Song." Sondra Lee (Tiger Lily in the Mary Martin *Peter Pan*), who performed a small role in the original production of *Reuben Reuben*, called "The Rose Song" "the most beautiful music I ever danced to in my life!"

The score for the Broadway musical *Juno* (based on Sean O'Casey's play *Juno and the Paycock*), which some (like Ethan Mordden) have called an opera, is one of the most beautiful ever written for Broadway, though it ran for only 16 performances there. Revivals at Williamstown, Long Wharf, and Vineyard Theatres have so far failed to spark the popularity its admirers know it deserves. Included here are a) the title number from Dawn Upshaw's hit CD, "I Wish It So" (which has also been recorded by Monte Amundsen, Judy Kaye, Rosemary Clooney, and Karen Holvik)—but in the version Blitzstein recorded singing and accompanying himself at the piano; b) the sung/spoken duet "One Kind Word" (created and recorded unforgettably on the original cast LP by Loren Driscoll, with Amundsen doing the speaking); c) the allegorical "Bird Upon the Tree" (which Amundsen sang with Shirley Booth in the title role).

The last three songs in this book, all from works that Blitzstein did not live to complete, were premiered posthumously, April 19, 1964, orchestrated by Hershy Kay, in a concert at Philharmonic Hall in New York conducted and introduced by Leonard Bernstein. *Sacco and Vanzetti*, a three-act opera commissioned by the Ford Foundation and optioned by the Metropolitan Opera, concerns a subject that had consumed Blitzstein for a third of a century: the 1927 execution in Massachusetts of two Italian anarchists who were most probably innocent of the crime for which they had been convicted. The aria, "With A Woman To Be," which Blitzstein developed from a fragment that had originally been part of *Reuben Reuben*, is best heard on the Premier recording, sung by Ronald Edwards, with piano.

Jose Ferrer sang "How I Met My New Grandfather" as a solo (though it was originally conceived, and appears here, as a duet) from the one-act opera *Idiots First* at that Philharmonic Hall concert with what Harold C. Schoenberg of the *New York Times* called "a Yiddish accent that would have made a row of blintzes stand up and salute." (Ferrer later said he'd at first felt insulted, then realized the comment was meant as a compliment!) This writer completed the opera in December, 1973. A few words and notes were changed in January, 1974 in accordance with the wishes of Bernstein and Malamud.. James Sergi won the International Singers Competition of the Center for Contemporary Opera with it. The 1978 New York City premiere of the opera (which Ned Rorem called Blitzstein's "best work") won the first Off-Broadway Opera Award for "most important event of the season." The orchestral premiere came in 1992, but the work has yet to receive its staged orchestral premiere. All performances of the complete opera, to date, have been paired with another opera based on a Malamud story, *Karla* (1974), by this writer, published by Theodore Presser together with *Idiots First* under the joint title (original with Blitzstein) *Tales of Malamud*. Other Malamud operas could also be part of a double or triple bill with it, specifically this writer's *Suppose A Wedding* (1996, also Presser) and Elie Siegmeister's *Angel Levine* and *The Lady of the Lake* (both 1985, Carl Fischer). Other one-act operas that have been or could be considered as companion pieces include Blitzstein's own *Triple Sec* (1928), *Parabola and Circula* (1929), *The Harpies* (1931, first performed only in 1953), and *I've Got the Tune* (1937), and Leonard Bernstein's *Trouble in Tahiti* (1952), which was dedicated to Blitzstein.

"Then," a prostitute's song like "The Nickel Under the Foot," is meant to be sung with a "purity" that is "hard-boiled," as the matchmaker's daughter awaits her date (and her fate?) with a rabbinical student. The libretto is complete, but aside from a sketch of Scene 1, this song is all that Blitzstein finished, musically, from his other projected Malamud opera, *The Magic Barrel*. But perhaps one day it too, along with *Sacco and Vanzetti* (see *Opera Journal* 29:1 (March, 1996) pp.26-46), will be completed and performed.

Acknowledgments: Robert J. Dietz, John Jansson, Emily R. Lehrman, Ralph Locke, Helene Williams, Anonymous.